The Haunted Baking Club

Maverick
Early Readers

'The Haunted Baking Club'
An original concept by Alison Donald
© Alison Donald

Illustrated by Kaley Mccabe

Published by MAVERICK ARTS PUBLISHING LTD
Studio 11, City Business Centre, 6 Brighton Road,
Horsham, West Sussex, RH13 5BB
© Maverick Arts Publishing Limited February 2021
+44 (0)1403 256941

A CIP catalogue record for this book is available at the British Library.

ISBN 978-1-84886-767-3

www.maverickbooks.co.uk

Gold

This book is rated as: Gold Band (Guided Reading)

The Haunted Baking Club

By **Alison Donald**

Illustrated by
Kaley Mccabe

Chapter 1

Sam knew that Cobblestone Primary was the right school for him the moment he walked through the door one year ago.

The school was on a lonely hill. It was dark and gloomy. There were cobwebs, and creaky floors. There was even a rumour that the school was haunted. Sam couldn't believe his good luck!

A haunted school was exactly where Sam wanted to be. Sam loved spooky places. He was a ghost hunter. And so was his best friend, Sarah.

Sam and Sarah kept a ghost-hunting log book. They were always watching and noticing things that others didn't.

For example, they noticed that Mrs Oddbottom was very organised but her papers often disappeared.

They noticed that the lights went out sometimes, and the caretaker had no idea why.

They also heard a lot of creaks in the hallways - but the floors weren't made of wood.

All of these things could only be caused by a ghost!

Together they had searched everywhere for the ghost. There was just one place they hadn't looked: the kitchen. If only they could get inside. But how?

Then, one day, something unexpected happened.

"We have a new after school club. It's a baking club. Who would like to join?" Mrs Oddbottom asked.

Sam glanced at Sarah and both their hands shot up in the air. Joining the baking club would allow them to ghost hunt in the kitchen!

"Perfect," said Mrs Oddbottom. "See you two after school."

Sam and Sarah grinned. Finally, they could search the kitchen for the ghost of Cobblestone Primary.

Chapter 2

Sam and Sarah rushed to the kitchen after class. "Remember," said Sam, "we have to pretend that we are here to bake."

"Got it," said Sarah.

Sam and Sarah were the only children at the Baking Club, which was lucky. It meant that they could ghost hunt without getting caught.

"Today we're making a chocolate cake," said Mrs Oddbottom. "Here's the recipe."

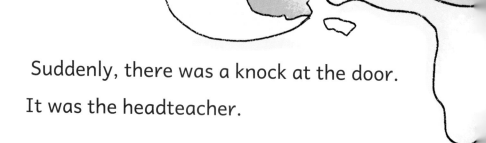

Suddenly, there was a knock at the door. It was the headteacher.

"Something's come up," said Mrs Oddbottom. "Get started and I'll be back as soon as I can."

Finally, Sam and Sarah were alone in the kitchen.

"Switch the lights off, Sam. The ghost might come out if it's dark."

Sam switched off the lights and they switched on their torches.

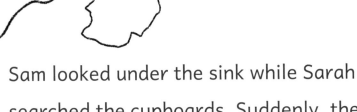

Sam looked under the sink while Sarah searched the cupboards. Suddenly, there was a TAP, TAP, TAP.

"What was that?" Sam cried.

Sarah shone her torch around. All the eggs were cracked open on the floor behind them.

"Look! The ghost must be here!" Sarah bent down to pick up the eggs when the sugar and flour started raining down.

"Who did that?" asked Sarah.

"It wasn't me," said Sam. "It was the ghost again!"

"The ghost must want our attention," Sarah decided.

Next the mixing bowls rose off the counter. It looked like the ghost was juggling them.

"This is so cool!" Sam said, as he took pictures for the ghost-hunting log book. Suddenly, Sam and Sarah heard the click-clack of Mrs Oddbottom's shoes.

The floor was covered in eggs, flour and sugar and the bowls were everywhere! Sarah switched on the lights.

"How will we explain this mess?" Sam panicked.

"I don't know!" Sarah cried.

They ran to meet Mrs Oddbottom at the door. "We can explain!" they said.

"Well, I am disappointed," Mrs Oddbottom said. Sarah and Sam knew they were in big trouble.

"You should have waited for me to put the cake in the oven. You could have burned yourselves. But otherwise, well done. I'm impressed you managed to ice the cake too!"

Sarah and Sam turned around. The mess had been cleared up and a three-layer chocolate cake was on the counter.

"Sorry Mrs Oddbottom," said Sarah. "It won't happen again. "

Just then the football club walked past. "What's that yummy smell?"

Sam and Sarah shared the cake with the football club. While everyone was chatting, Sam whispered to Sarah, "The ghost is a good baker!"

Chapter 3

Sam and Sarah held a ghost-hunting club meeting at Sarah's house.

"Here is what we know about the ghost in the kitchen," said Sarah. She made a list:

1)   It is trying to get our attention
2)   It is a very good baker
3)   It lives in the kitchen

"Here is a list of things we *don't* know about the ghost..."

1)   Why is it here?
2)   Who is it?
3)   What is it trying to tell us?

Sam and Sarah scratched their heads. The ghost was lurking in the kitchen for a reason, they just knew it! And it was a kind ghost who loved to bake. Sam and Sarah couldn't wait to find out more.

Chapter 4

The next week at Baking Club, Sarah and Sam could hardly wait for Mrs Oddbottom to leave. And, just like clockwork, the headteacher knocked and needed Mrs Oddbottom's help again.

"Quick, let's look for clues," said Sarah. "Maybe there is a clue in the kitchen that will tell us why the baking ghost is here and what it is trying to tell us."

Sam and Sarah laughed while they searched. The baking ghost was trying to get their attention again by spinning pie dough in the air and whirring cake mix in the blender.

"Baking Ghost, you are so funny! But why are you here? What do you need to tell us?" Sam asked.

Suddenly Sarah cried, "Look! I've found a clue!"

Sarah had found a secret cupboard. Inside was an old piece of newspaper folded up.

"Open it!" said Sam.

1935 - John Cobblestone founded a soup kitchen at his house on Spider Hill. He offered food and kindness to anyone who came through the doors. He never turned anyone away. His house was filled with laughter and delicious food, always.

"Spider Hill?" said Sam. "That's where we are! So, years ago, this used to be a soup kitchen: a place that fed hungry people for free."

"And Cobblestone Primary," said Sarah, "must be named after John Cobblestone."

"Maybe the kitchen ghost wants us to feed people in need just like John Cobblestone did. Maybe the ghost is John Cobblestone himself!"

They heard the click-clack of Mrs Oddbottom's shoes. The kitchen was suddenly tidied up and an apple pie and a rainbow cake were finished and on the cooling rack.

Mrs Oddbottom looked cross. "I told you both not to use the oven when I'm not here," she scolded.

"We're sorry, Mrs Oddbottom," said Sam.

"We just got carried away," Sarah sighed.

Mrs Oddbottom's face softened. She helped herself to a slice of cake.

"This is delicious!" she announced.

"Thanks!" said Sarah. She nudged Sam. Now that Mrs Oddbottom had calmed down, it was time to say something.

"We have an idea, Mrs Oddbottom," said Sam.

"Maybe you can help," Sarah added.

Chapter 5

Sam and Sarah started to bake more and more food. Every Friday, with Mrs Oddbottom's help, they held a bake sale. The whole school crowded around to buy freshly baked goods.

Each week, Sam, Sarah and the baking ghost baked cakes, cinnamon buns, bread, cookies, and pies. Students and teachers loved them.

After the first bake sale, Sam and Sarah were amazed. "We've made over one hundred pounds!" they cried.

But the money wasn't for them. Each week, they gave the money to a charity that provided food, clothing and shelter for families in need.

Sam and Sarah had a warm feeling inside; they weren't just making cakes for fun anymore. They were helping people.

Sam and Sarah stopped searching for ghost clues and started to bake more. The baking ghost seemed happy with their new hobby. Each week, it was quieter and quieter until Sam and Sarah were doing all of the baking themselves.

Soon, more and more children joined the baking club.

Cobblestone Primary wasn't haunted anymore. Mrs Oddbottom's papers never disappeared. The lights stopped going out for no reason. There were no more creaks in the hallways, and it didn't look gloomy.

Sam and Sarah now spent most of their spare time baking, but they still talked about ghosts. They had solved the mystery of the baking ghost, and now the school was full of yummy baking smells, kindness and laughter.

But every once in a while, Sam and Sarah did wonder if the baking ghost gave them a helping hand.

The End

Book Bands for Guided Reading

The Institute of Education book banding system is a scale of colours that reflects the various levels of reading difficulty. The bands are assigned by taking into account the content, the language style, the layout and phonics. Word, phrase and sentence level work is also taken into consideration.

Maverick Early Readers are a bright, attractive range of books covering the pink to white bands. All of these books have been book banded for guided reading to the industry standard and edited by a leading educational consultant.

To view the whole Maverick Readers scheme, visit our website at
www.maverickearlyreaders.com

Or scan the QR code above to view our scheme instantly!

Pink
Red
Yellow
Blue
Green
Orange
Turquoise
Purple
Gold
White